Reflections of LOVE

Coloring Book Therapy for Grief & Loss
by April McCallum

ISBN: 978-1-7325752-7-1

Reflections of Love: Coloring Book Therapy for Grief and Loss

© 2018 by April McCallum

Published in the United States by Heart & Key Publishing

Heart & Key
PUBLISHING

Cover Design Collaboration and Colorization by Pete Berg

www.aprilmccallumdesigns.com

Welcome!

Art and Heart... I'm grateful you found your way here, but I am so sorry for the loss that brought you to this place. This collection of coloring pages was created with love, just for you. It's a combination of beautiful and powerful hand-drawn illustrations, verses and quotes. A creative companion to accompany you on your very personal journey through grief and loss.

Reflections of Love was designed to give you a peaceful, comforting and therapeutic coloring experience. I hope it will fill your mind and heart with positive loving reflection, gratitude, and hope for the future. As you turn the pages, you will find a variety of whimsically-styled meaningful pictures and quotes to color with themes familiar to those navigating the difficult season of loss.

"The risk of love is loss, and the price of loss is grief — but the pain of grief is only a shadow when compared with the pain of never risking love." — Hilary Stanton Zunin

Tips: You will notice a bit of extra margin on the binding side. I intentionally designed it that way for ease of maneuvering. If you would like to practice your lines and coloring tools, you will find a blank page in the back of the book to do just that. If you plan to use non-dry coloring materials, please place a blank sheet or two under the page you're coloring so it won't bleed through.

When it comes to art and therapeutic coloring, it's all about the heart. There is no right or wrong, good or bad. Consider this book a place for you "to go" to get lost in mindful healing thoughts and color.

Sending out Heart Hugs!

XO
April

Grief is like the OCEAN
it comes on waves ebbing and flowing
Sometimes the water is calm,
and sometimes it is overwhelming
all we can do is learn to swim
Vicki Harrison

Heaven cannot heal that
EARTH has no source

THOMAS MOORE

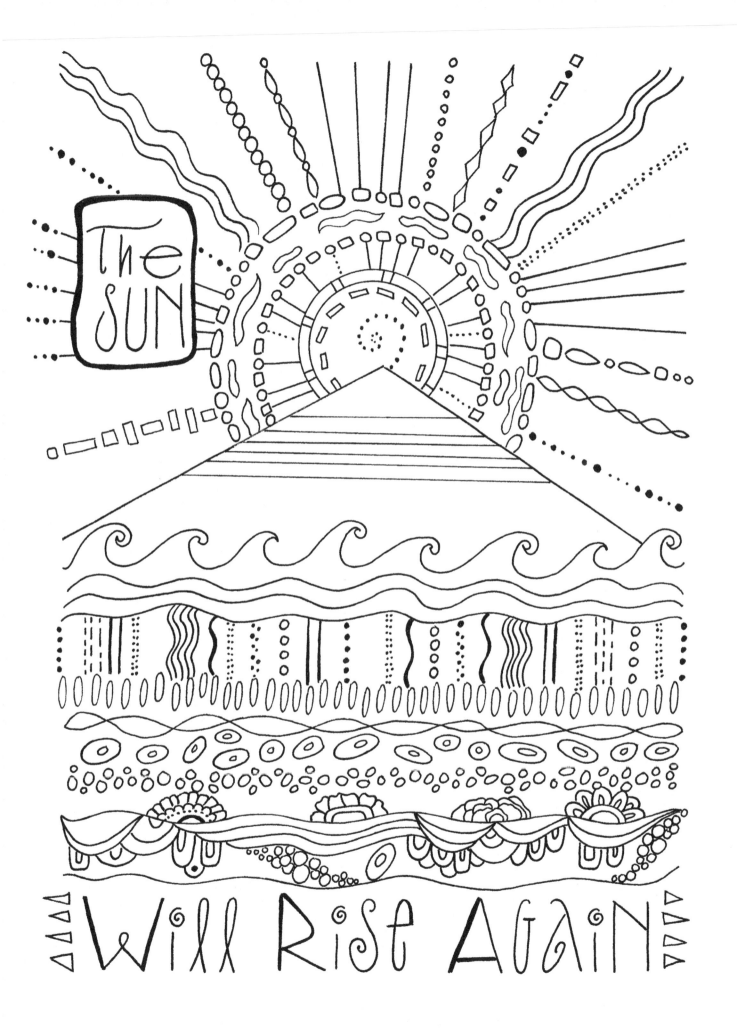

Broken hearts
are Mended one Stitch

LOVE

of LOVE at a time

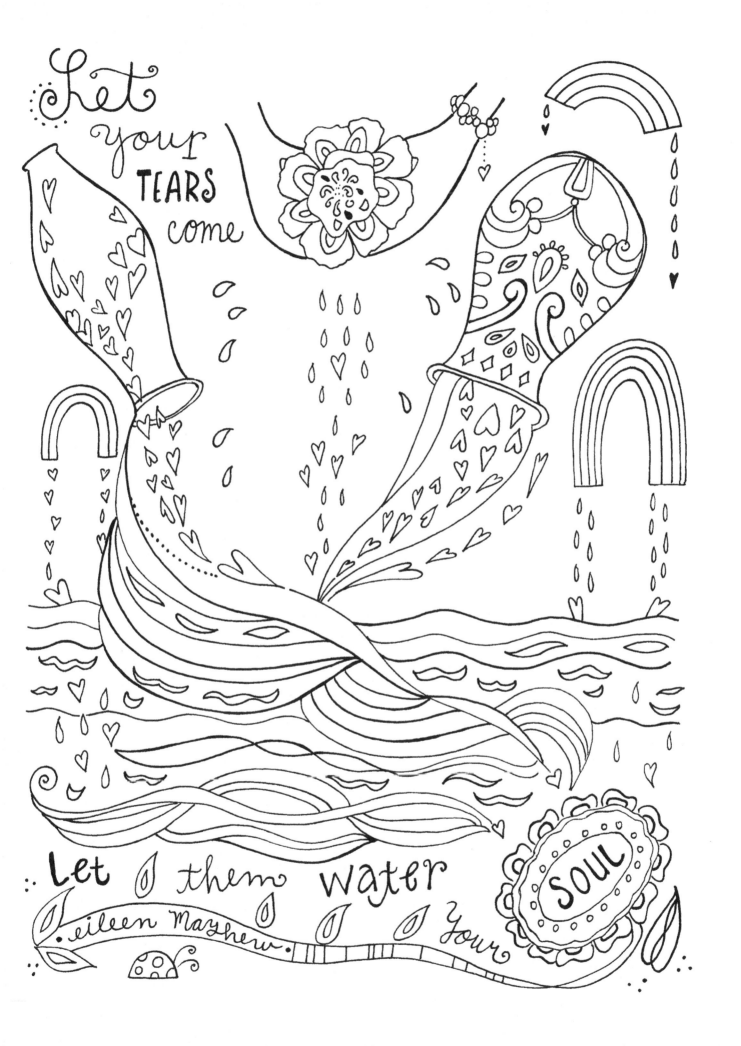

Faith Hope Love

"Sorrow looks back
Worry looks around
Faith looks up"

Ralph Waldo Emerson

There is a sacredness in tears. They are not the mark of weakness, but of POWER. They speak more eloquently than ten thousand tongues. They ARE messengers of overwhelming GRIEF... and unspeakable love.

—Washington Irving

unspeakable love

each PERSON'S GRieF has its own fingerprint

JOHN MARK GREEN

YOU are my hiding place you will protect Me from Trouble and surround me with SONGS of deliverance

Psalm 32:7

Spring always comes after the FROST

All of Our lives are a MOSAIC of sadness & loss, Beauty and joy

Grief is the price we pay for love

love

·QUEEN ELIZABETH II·

a star fell from the sky in the storm and there was great darkness

but when i awoke, it was a NEW day and a

rainbow became my canopy of

Hope

Shared JOY is a double joy.

Shared Sorrow is half a Sorrow

SWEDISH PROVERB

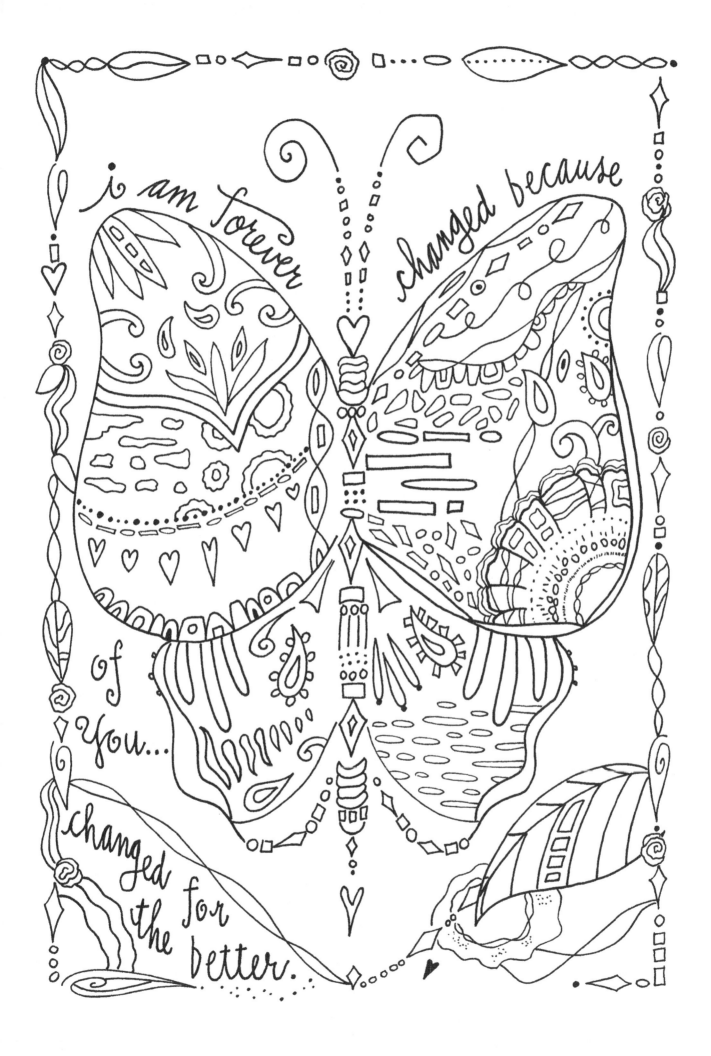

express yourself

a poem, a thought,
a prayer...

*L*ife is eternal,

and love is immortal,

and death is only a horizon,

and a horizon is nothing

save the limit of our sight.

– William Penn

A Little About April...

April McCallum is an illustrator, cartoonist and writer. Since retiring from a successful career in the high-tech industry, she's focused her creative passions on art, writing and advocacy projects. Her artwork has been licensed and featured on magazine covers, for business and non-profits, and on a variety of gift products. Her writing and artwork has appeared in a variety of magazines and featured on CNBC. Her signature style combines words and visuals, color and design. Her writing and illustration work is inspirational, hope-filled and empowering, while her cartoonist side brings a unique twist to the table.

April has long been an advocacy artist designing creative pieces that interweave words and visuals to speak to issues close to her heart. Current topics include grief and loss, adoption, empowering women, breast cancer awareness, human trafficking and violence against women.

Pete Berg and April McCallum have been creative collaborators on a variety of colorful and interesting projects over the years. If you would like to connect with Pete Berg regarding a graphic art project, he can be reached at: ohberg3@gmail.com.

Website:	www.aprilmccallumdesigns.com
Email:	april@aprilmccallumdesigns.com
Facebook:	@AprilMcCallumDesigns
Instagram:	@AprilCartoons	@AprilLovesColor
Twitter:	@AprilCartoons	@PinkCartoons
Pinterest:	https://www.pinterest.com/aprilmccallum/
	https://www.pinterest.com/pinkpassionlife/

PRACTICE

PAGE

Made in United States
North Haven, CT
02 June 2023

37278963R00063